VELJO TORMIS

EESTI KALENDRILAULUD
ESTONIAN CALENDAR SONGS

1. MARDILAULUD / MARTINMAS SONGS
MEESKOORILE / FOR MALE CHORUS

2. KADRILAULUD / ST. CATHERINE'S DAY SONGS
NAISKOORILE / FOR FEMALE CHORUS

3. VASTLALAULUD / SHROVETIDE SONGS
MEESKOORILE / FOR MALE CHORUS

4. KIIGELAULUD / SWING SONGS
NAISKOORILE / FOR FEMALE CHORUS

5. JAANILAULUD / ST. JOHN'S DAY SONGS
NAIS- JA MEESKOORILE / FOR COMBINED FEMALE AND MALE CHORUSES

 FENNICA GEHRMAN

SISUKORD / CONTENTS

Algmaterjal kogumikust «Eesti rahvalaule viisidega II» (Koostanud Herbert Tampere).
Eesti Riiklik Kirjastus, Tallinn 1960.

As source material, the composer has used a collection of Estonian folk songs with melodies «Eesti rahvalaule viisidega», vol. 2, compiled by Herbert Tampere (Eesti Riiklik Kirjastus, Tallinn 1960).

Cover design and map by Kersti Tormis

Kolmas osa sarjast "Eesti kalendrilaulud" nais- ja meeskoorile

VASTLALAULUD

Tsükkel eesti rahvalaule meeskoorile

The third part of the series "Estonian Calendar Songs" for female and male choruses

Songs of the Shrove Tuesday

A cycle of Estonian folk songs for male chorus

Texts: traditional (in Estonian), translated and adapted by Ritva Poom

1. Vistel - vastel *(Simuna)*
Vistel - Vastel (from *Simuna* parish)

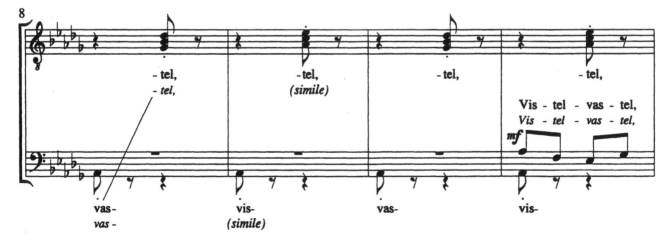

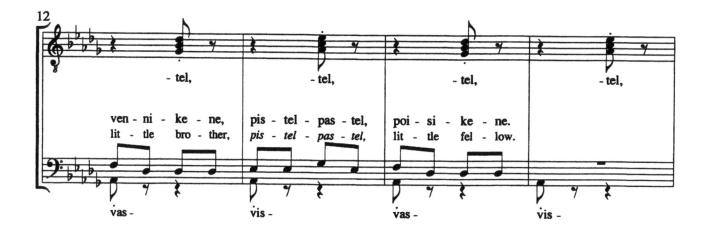

-tel,   -tel,   -tel,   -tel,

ven - ni - ke - ne,   pis - tel - pas - tel,   poi - si - ke - ne.
lit - tle   bro - ther,   *pis - tel - pas - tel,*   *lit - tle   fel - low.*

vas -   vis -   vas -   vis -

sub. f   *p*

-tel.   Ei   vas - tel   to - as - sa   is - tu,   - tel,
        No, Shrove-tide   does   not   sit   in - side,

vas -   vis -

f

- tel,   vas - tel   va - hib   vai - ni' - ul - la,
         vas - tel   wat - ches   o'er   the   com - mons,

vas -

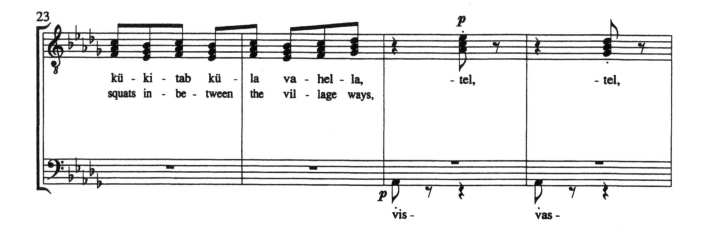

p

kü - ki - tab kü - la   va - hel - la,   - tel,   - tel,
squats in - be - tween   the   vil - lage ways,

p   vis -   vas -

kül - ma - kin - da' - ad kä - es - sa, kül - ma - kir - jad kin - nas - tes - sa,
wear - ing mit - tens of frost, mit - tens, fros - ty fi - gures on the mit - tens,

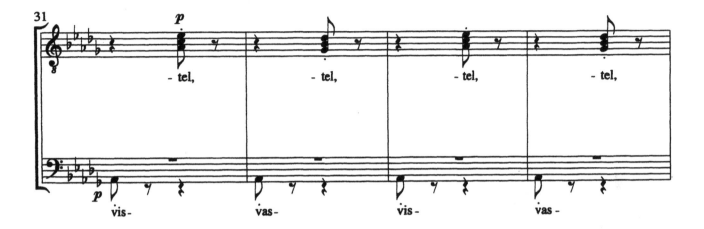

- tel, - tel, - tel, - tel,

vis - vas - vis - vas -

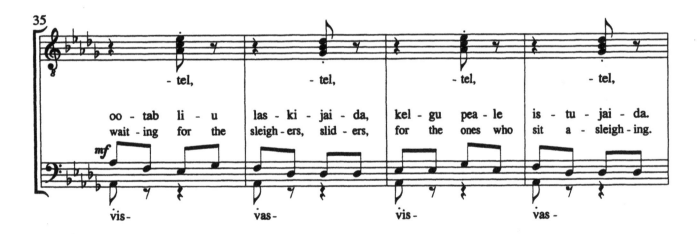

- tel, - tel, - tel, - tel,

oo - tab li - u las - ki - jai - da, kel - gu pea - le is - tu - jai - da.
wait - ing for the sleigh - ers, slid - ers, for the ones who sit a - sleigh - ing.

vis - vas - vis - vas -

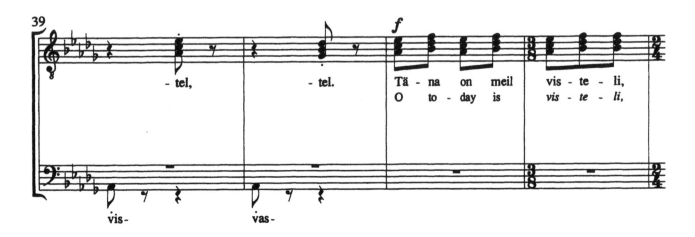

- tel, - tel. Tä - na on meil vis - te - li,
O to - day is vis - te - li,

vis - vas -

5

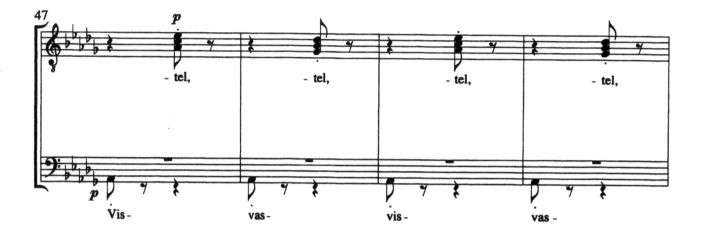

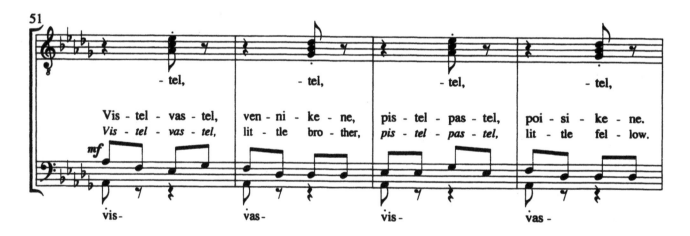

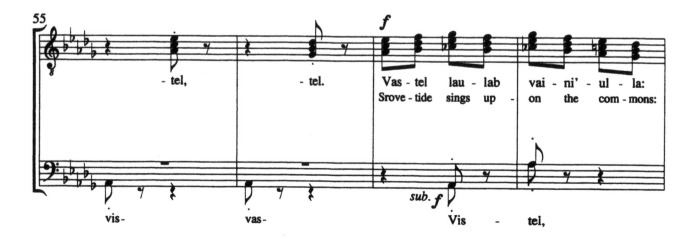

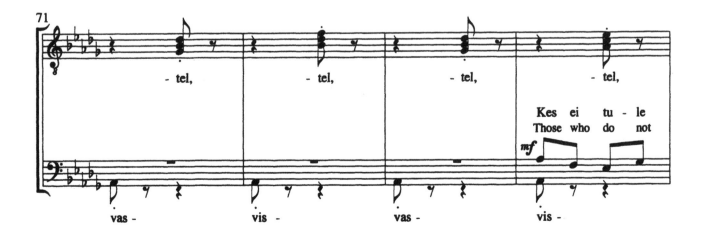

7

- tel,   - tel,   - tel,   - tel,   - tel,

liu - gu lask - ma, sel li - nad li - gu - je jää - gu,
come a - sleigh - ing, may their flax lie e - ver soak - ing,

vas -   vis -   vas -   vis -   vas -

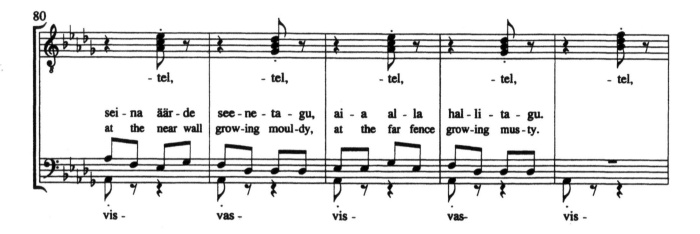

- tel,   - tel,   - tel,   - tel,   - tel,

sei - na äär - de see - ne - ta - gu, ai - a al - la hal - li - ta - gu.
at the near wall grow - ing moul - dy, at the far fence grow - ing mus - ty.

vis -   vas -   vis -   vas -   vis -

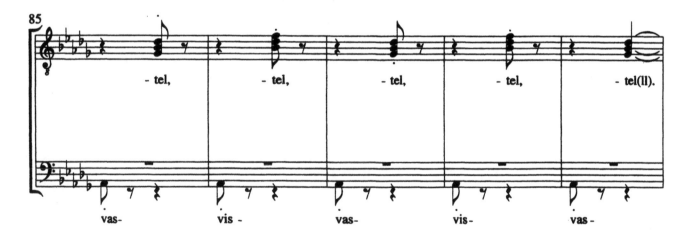

- tel,   - tel,   - tel,   - tel,   - tel(ll).

vas -   vis -   vas -   vis -   vas -

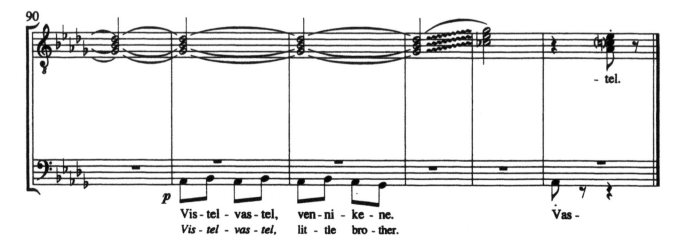

- tel.

p

Vis - tel - vas - tel, ven - ni - ke - ne.   Vas -
Vis - tel - vas - tel, lit - tle bro - ther.

8

2. Lina loitsimine (*Paistu*)

Spell Upon Flax (from *Paistu* parish)

* Staggered breathing to the end (phrases should be linked without any simultaneous caesuras for breathing).

3. Liulaskmise - laul *(Sangaste)*

Sledding Song *(from Sangaste parish)*

liu - ge, lau - ge, kui sii rii tii - ke - ne,
liu - ge, lau - ge, long as sleigh run - ners' slid - ing

liu - ge, lau - ge,
liu - ge, lau - ge,

liu - ge, lau - ge, liu - ge -
liu - ge, lau - ge, liu - ge -

liu - ge, lau - ge, liu - ge, lau - ge, liu - ge,
liu - ge, lau - ge, liu - ge, lau - ge, liu - ge,

- eeh, aah, ooh!
- eeh, aah, ooh!

lau - ge - eeh, aah, ooh!
lau - ge - eeh, aah, ooh!

gliss. lungo

Allegro molto ♩ = 168

Liuu - uh - uh - uh! Uh! Uu -
Liuu - uh - uh - uh! Uh! Uu -

Uu -
Uu -

gliss. lungo

Liuu - uh - uh - uh! Uh! Köst - ri li - na
Liuu - uh - uh - uh! Uh! Sex - ton's flax to

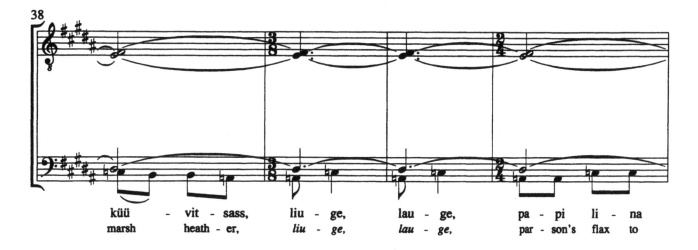

küü - vit - sass,   liu - ge,   lau - ge,   pa - pi   li - na
marsh   heath - er,   *liu - ge,   lau - ge,*   par - son's   flax   to

pa - ju - piit - sass,   liu - ge,   lau - ge!   Uu -
reed   thin   wil - low,   *liu - ge,   lau - ge!   Uu -*

Moderato

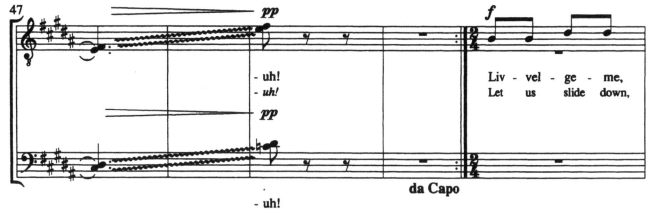

- uh!   Liv - vel - ge - me,
- uh!   Let   us   slide   down,

da Capo

- uh!
- uh!

lav - vel - ge - me,   liu - ge,   lau - ge!
let   us   glide   down,   *liu - ge,   lau - ge!*

liu - ge,   lau - ge!
liu - ge,   lau - ge!

The Estonian Calendar Songs

A note by the composer

I was born at Kuusalu near Tallinn (the capital of Estonia) on 7 August 1930. I got the speciality of a composer from the Moscow Conservatoire (1951-1956), having previously studied the organ, choral conducting and composition in Tallinn. I have taught at the Tallinn Music School and worked in the Estonian Composers' Union. Since 1969, I have been a freelance composer.

The most essential part of my works is choral music, the most essential part of which, in its turn, is connected with the ancient folk song of Estonians and other Finnic peoples. The best-known compositions in this field are the incantation Curse Upon Iron (Raua needmine) and the extended series Estonian Calendar Songs (Eesti kalendrilaulud) and Forgotten Peoples (Unustatud rahvad, on the motifs of Livonian, Votic, Izhorian, Ingrian Finnish, Vepsian and Karelian folklore). All in all, I have written about 60 cycles or series, about 40 extended choral works and about 80 songs for a cappella choir. In other genres, Overture No. 2 for symphony orchestra, the opera Swan's Flight (Luigelend) and the cantata-ballet Estonian Ballads (Eesti ballaadid) have gained wide critical acclaim.

I consider, the Estonian Calendar Songs as a turning point in my artistic life. Prior to that, I had been following the example of the outstanding composers of the previous generation – Mart Saar, Cyrillus Kreek, Eduard Tubin. I had been using folk tunes as the source material for thematic-intonational development, for creating the musical "mother tongue". Now, I discovered for myself the Estonian ancient runo songs as a synchretic phenomenon which, besides the melody and words, comprises a specific form and a manner of performance, and the social function of song – an integral part of a nation's life. Yet my music can by no means be labelled as folk or world music. It is rather an attempt to preserve the authenticity of the source material, making a compromise with the forms and performing opportunities of modern philharmonic music. Therefore, it is classical choral music.

Veljo Tormis

Veljo Tormis - Estonian Calendar Songs

The series of five choral cycles by Veljo Tormis *Estonian Calendar Songs* (1966 - 67), has a special place in his output as well as in Estonian music in general. The genre of a largescale choral composition had emerged during the first half of this century, due to the important role of the choral movement and choir conductors in the history of Estonian national music. Young Tormis continued the tradition and before the mid - - 1960's he had composed several successful cycles of choral songs using folk tunes as melodic material. In *Estonian Calendar Songs,* however, the romantic attitude towards folklore as thematic material for developing national style in music was replaced by much more powerful feelings and original compositional ideas. Tormis discovered how to transform into art music the primeval enchanting force of prechristian ritual songs. That was the starting point for the "real" Tormis style as we know it now, thirty years later, and several cycles of great choral compositions based on ancient folk songs of different peoples followed (*Livonian Heritage* in 1970, *Votic Wedding Songs* in 1971, and many others). No more did Tormis use a folk tune as a melodic idea for further motivic development. Instead, old rustic songs sounded in his compositions in their original manner, but around those those monotonously repeated short tunes he built truly symphonic choral textures and dramatic musical structures. This description may recall Stravinsky's *The Rite of Spring,* but the sound of Tormis's choral compositions is certainly closer to Ligeti's static textural blocks or the repetitive music of more recent composers. Tormis is a real master of choral sound.

Traditional Estonian calendar songs

The ancestors of modern Estonians, Baltic - Finnic tribes living on the southern coast of the Finnish Gulf, were christianized in the 13th century by the German and Danish invaders. The new rulers not only brought Christian religion, but also made the local people, free farmers and sailors, their serfs. However, social and spiritual distance between the German-speaking upper classes and the Estonian peasants, or countrypeople as they called themselves, helped the old prechristian beliefs and rituals, together with their songs, survive through the centuries. Old Estonian folk songs contain words and linguistic forms that have long ago disappeared from spoken Estonian. Calendar songs belonged to the seasonal rituals of an ancient farming people. The Estonian folk calendar is a peculiar mixture of Catholic and prechristian tradition. Most of the names of feasts originate in the church calendar, but the customs and beliefs go back to earlier times. The traditions of calendar feasts have survived from elements of ancient fertility rites that were aimed at protecting the harvest and the cattle. The texts of those songs reflect belief in the magic power of words.

Urve Lippus

Shrovetide Songs

Vastlapäev, "Shrove Tuesday", marks the beginning of Lent. It is a movable feast following the church calendar (forty working days before Easter) which always falls on the Tuesday of the new moon. In the folk calendar, the beliefs and customs connected with this day do not originate from the church.

It was a custom all over Estonia to go sledding on Shrove Tuesday, it being commonly believed that the longer the sled slid, the taller the flax would grow. One could coast down a hill on a pot cover, on a split log, or on anything else available; in modern times it would obviously be a small sled. If the neighbourhood was flat, people harnessed a horse to a sledge or sleigh, and took a ride (again, the longer the ride, the taller the flax). On the sea coast, people cleared the snow off the ice, hammered a log in the centre, fixed a revolving pole to the log, a small sled to the other end of the pole - and thus built a " merry-go-round on ice" to have a Shrovetide ride.

During the slide or ride would resound the cry *Lina liugu, pikka kiudu!*, "Slide for flax, for fibres long!". With time, these calls developed into songs inviting all to join in, chiding those who would not, and wishing for a good crop of flax.

The first song presented here is from north Estonia (from Simuna parish), two others are from the south (the second from Paistu and the third from Sangaste parish).

Ülo Tedre